Peter Pan
and Peter Pan in Kensington Gardens